Presented to :

_____

From :

_____

Date :

_____

Also by Helen Steiner Rice

HEART GIFTS

LOVINGLY

PRAYERFULLY

SOMEONE CARES

Story of the Christmas Guest

as retold by

Helen Steiner Rice

Fleming H. Revell Company
Old Tappan, New Jersey

A personal message

Library of Congress Cataloging in Publication Data

Rice, Helen Steiner.
    The story of the Christmas guest.
    I. Title.
PS3568.I28S7   811'.5'4   72-1754
ISBN 0-8007-0544-0

Printed in the United States of America

This Lovely Legend
        is centuries old,
    repeated, rewritten,
        REVISED and RETOLD...
And through countless ages
        this story survives
As Christmas rekindles,
        renews and revives
Man's longing to look
        in the dear Lord's face
And bask in the warmth
        of His love and His grace,
Not knowing each day
        that He comes disguised
And begs to be welcomed
        and recognized...
But unperceivingly
        we turn HIM away,
Not expecting "THIS GUEST"
        on a routine day...
But the "SHOELESS BEGGAR"
        and the "BENT OLD CRONE"
And the "HOMELESS CHILD"
        so lost and alone
Come daily and knock at
        "THE DOOR of OUR HEART"
But we are too busy,
        and unseen "THEY" depart...
And man goes on searching
        year after year
Hoping that someday
        THE LORD will appear!

Helen Steiner Rice

The story of the Christmas Guest

as retold by

Helen Steiner Rice

When I was a child I loved to hear
    This story my Grandma told each year,
She told it in her native tongue,
    And I was very, very young...
But yet this story seemed to be
    Filled with wonderment for me,
For in my childish heart there grew
    The dream that I might see Him, too,
For He might call on me this way
    So I must watch for Him each day...
And that is why "The Christmas Guest"
    Is still the story I love best—
And I retell it to you now,
    For I can't help but feel somehow
That children Everywhere should hear
    The story Grandma told each year...
For Christmas Day is doubly blest
    When Jesus is Our Christmas Guest!

It happened one day
    at the year's white end,
Two neighbors called
    on an old-time friend
And they found his shop
    so meager and mean,
Made gay with a thousand
    boughs of green,

And Conrad was sitting
with face a-shine
When he suddenly stopped
as he stitched a twine

*A*nd said, "Old friends,
at dawn today,
When the cock was crowing
the night away,
The Lord appeared
in a dream to me
And said, 'I am coming
your guest to be' ...

So I've been busy
        with feet astir,
Strewing my shop
        with branches of fir,
The table is spread
        and the kettle is shined
And over the rafters
        the holly is twined,

_A_nd now I will wait
for my Lord to appear
And listen closely
so I will hear
His step as He nears
my humble place
And I open the door
and look in His face"...

So his friends went home
and left Conrad alone,
For this was the happiest
day he had known,
For, long since, his family
had passed away
And Conrad had spent
a sad Christmas Day...

ut he knew with the Lord
as his Christmas guest
This Christmas would be
the dearest and best,

And he listened with only
joy in his heart,
And with every sound
he would rise with a start
And look for the Lord
to be standing there
In answer to
his earnest prayer...

*S*o he ran to the window
after hearing a sound,
But all that he saw
on the snow-covered ground
Was a shabby beggar
whose shoes were torn
And all of his clothes
were ragged and worn...

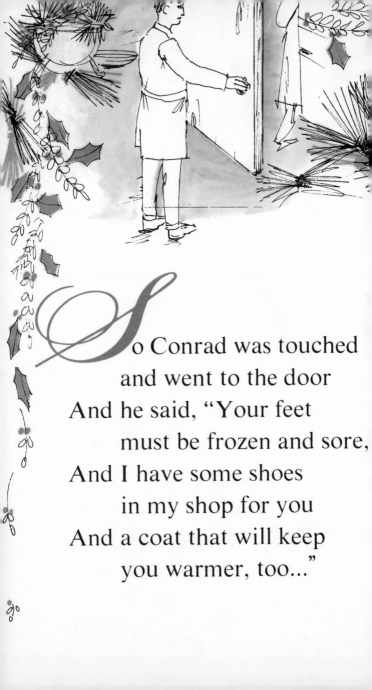

So Conrad was touched
   and went to the door
And he said, "Your feet
      must be frozen and sore,
And I have some shoes
      in my shop for you
And a coat that will keep
      you warmer, too..."

So with grateful heart
the man went away,
But as Conrad noticed
the time of day
He wondered what made
the dear Lord so late
And how much longer
he'd have to wait,

hen he heard a knock
and ran to the door,
But it was only
a stranger once more,
A bent, old crone
with a shawl of black,
A bundle of faggots
piled on her back.

*S*he asked for only
    a place to rest,
But that was reserved
    for Conrad's Great Guest...
But her voice seemed to plead,
    "Don't send me away,
Let me rest for awhile
    on Christmas Day,"

So Conrad brewed her
a steaming cup
And told her to sit
at the table and sup...

But after she left
    he was filled with dismay
For he saw that the hours
    were passing away
And the Lord had not come
    as He said He would,
And Conrad felt sure
    he had misunderstood...

When out of the stillness
      he heard a cry,
"Please help me
      and tell me where am I,"
So again he opened
      his friendly door
And stood disappointed
      as twice before.

*I*t was only a child
    who had wandered away
And was lost from her family
    on Christmas Day...

Again Conrad's heart
was heavy and sad,
But he knew he should make
this little child glad,
So he called her in
and wiped her tears
And quieted all
her childish fears...

hen he led her back
to her home once more
But as he entered
his own darkened door
He knew that the Lord
was not coming today
For the hours of Christmas
had passed away...
So he went to his room
and knelt down to pray
And he said, "Dear Lord,
why did You delay,
What kept You from coming
to call on me,
For I wanted so much
Your face to see"...

When soft in the silence
 a voice he heard
"Lift up your head
 for I kept My word—
Three times My shadow
 crossed your floor—
Three times I came
 to your lonely door—

*F*or I was the beggar
      with bruised, cold feet,
I was the woman
      you gave to eat,
And I was the child
      on the homeless street."

Unaware, we pass "Him" by

On life's busy thoroughfares
We meet with ANGELS unawares—
But we are too busy to listen or hear,
Too busy to sense that God is near,
Too busy to stop and recognize
The grief that lies in another's eyes,
Too busy to offer to help or share,
Too busy to sympathize or care,
Too busy to do the GOOD THINGS we should,
Telling ourselves we would if we could ...
But life is too swift and the pace is too great
And we dare not pause for we might be late
For our next appointment which means so much,
We are willing to brush off the Saviour's touch
And we tell ourselves there will come a day
We will have more time to pause on our way ...
But before we know it "life's sun has set"
And we've passed the Saviour but never met,
For hurrying along life's thoroughfare
We passed Him by and remained unaware
That within the VERY SIGHT OF OUR EYE,
UNNOTICED, THE SON OF GOD PASSED BY.

Helen Steiner Rice